THE FOX
AND THE CROW

A fox once saw a crow fly off with a piece of cheese.

The fox was hungry
and the cheese looked
delicious.

He called out to the crow and wished him, "Good Morning."

He asked the crow to give him some of the cheese.

The crow shook his head in refusal. It meant a no.

The crow knew how clever the fox was.
He kept calm.

The cunning fox did not give up. He came up with a plan.

"What lovely shiny black feathers you have!" He flattered the crow. The crow was surprised.

"And what a wonderful voice you have!" the fox continued.

He then asked the crow to sing a song. The crow could not say no.

The crow swelled with pride and cleared his throat.

He thought of a song,
and opened his mouth
to sing.

And lo! The cheese slipped from his beak and fell on the ground.

The fox pounced upon it and gobbled it up! The crow looked on helplessly!